BEST OF
The Eagles

Production: Miranda Steel
Cover design by Glide Designs
Cover photograph supplied by Redferns
Published 1998

© International Music Publications Limited
Griffin House 161 Hammersmith Road London W6 8BS England

Best Of My Love

Words and Music by
Glenn Frey, Don Henley and
John David Souther

Ev - er - y night _ I'm ly - in' in bed, _ hold - in' you close _ in my
Beau - ti - ful faces and loud emp - ty places, look at the way that we

dreams; _ think - in' a - bout _ all the things that we _ said _ and
live; _ wast - in' our time _ on cheap talk and wine

Hotel California

Words and Music by
Don Felder, Glenn Frey and
Don Henley

Desperado

Words and Music by
Don Henley and Glenn Frey

17

Journey Of The Sorcerer

Words and Music by
Bernie Leadon

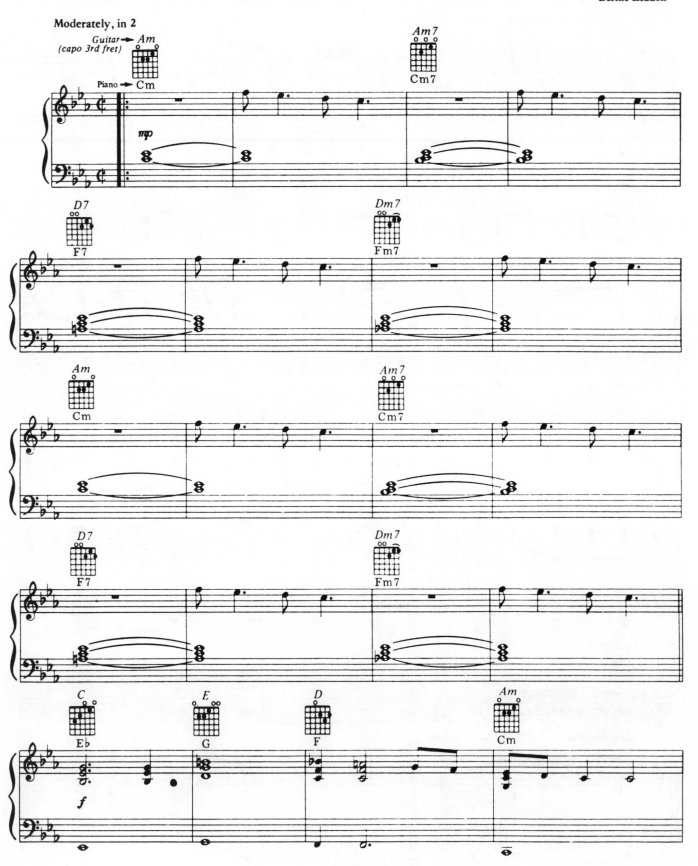

Life In The Fast Lane

Words and Music by
Glenn Frey, Don Henley and
Joe Walsh

Life in the fast lane sure-ly make you lose your mind.

Life in the fast lane, mm.

Are you with me so far?

Life in the fast lane; ev-'ry-thing all the time.

D. S. 𝄋 *(no repeats) al Coda* 𝄌

They did - n't care. They were just dy - in' to get off. And it was

Coda

Life in the fast__ lane.

Life in the fast__ lane.

Repeat and fade

Repeat and fade

Love Will Keep Us Alive

Words and Music by
Jim Capaldi, Paul Carrack and
Peter Vale

32

Lyin' Eyes

Words and Music by
Glenn Frey and Don Henley

One Of These Nights

Words and Music by
Don Henley and Glenn Frey

The full moon is call-ing, the fe-ver is high___ and the
I've been search-ing for the daugh-ter of the dev-il him-self;___ I've been

wick-ed wind whis-pers and moans.___ You got your de-mons,
search-ing for an an-gel in white.___ I've been wait-ing for a wom-an who's a

you got de-sires;___ well, I___ got a few of my own.___
lit-tle of both,_ and I can feel her but she's no-where in sight.___

42

Take It Easy

Words and Music by
Jackson Browne and Glenn Frey

Moderate Country feeling

New Kid In Town

Words and Music by
Glenn Frey, Don Henley and
John David Souther

Ooh,___ hoo.   Ev-'ry-bod-y's walk-ing like the

new kid   in town.   There's a   new kid   in town.

I don't want to hear it. There's a   new kid   in town.   I___ don't want to hear it. There's a

Repeat and fade

new kid   in town.   There's a   new kid   in town.   There's a

Take It To The Limit

Words and Music by
Randy Meisner, Don Henley and
Glenn Frey

58

Tequila Sunrise

Words and Music by
Glenn Frey and Don Henley

62